HAMPTON COURT
ART for LONDON TRANSPORT
COLOURING BOOK

MW00366766

Hampton Court was the favourite palace of England's King Henry VIII (reigned 1509–1547), who spent enormous sums of money turning it into one of the most magnificent palaces in his realm. About three centuries later Queen Victoria opened the palace and its gardens to visitors, creating a major public attraction.

In 1908, a man named Frank Pick was given responsibility for publicising the city of London's transport system, known as the Underground. He began commissioning artists to produce posters encouraging the public to use the system. He believed the posters could also enrich the quality of life in the city.

During the 1920s and 1930s, these posters reached a peak of stylistic quality. Designing a poster for the Underground became an honour among both great and aspiring artists. Pick was aware that almost every attraction in London, including Hampton Court, was within reach of the Underground. Eye-catching posters enticed travellers indirectly, by focussing on the destination rather than the mode of travel.

In this colouring book, you will find 22 posters featuring Hampton Court. The posters were created for the Underground by many different artists; the originals are shown as small pictures on the inside front and back covers. When you colour in these pictures, you can try to copy the original colours and style, or you might decide to use your own.

The last page of this book is blank so that you can draw and colour in your own picture. Imagine your house as a grand English castle, and see if you can capture it on the page.

UNDERGROUND

Pomegranate kids®
AGES 3 to 103!

1. John Hassall, *Hampton Court*, 1910 (detail). Double Crown Poster, 50.8 x 76.2 cm (20 x 30 in.).
2. Charles Paine, *Hampton Court*, 1921. Double Crown Poster, 50.8 x 76.2 cm (20 x 30 in.).
3. Dorothy Paton, *By Tram to Hampton Court*, 1927 (detail). Double Crown Poster, 50.8 x 76.2 cm (20 x 30 in.).
4. Arthur Blunt, *Hampton Court by Tram*, 1913. Double Crown Poster, 50.8 x 76.2 cm (20 x 30 in.).
5. Charles Paine, *Hampton Court by Tram*, 1922 (detail). Double Crown Poster, 50.8 x 76.2 cm (20 x 30 in.).
6. Charles Ernest Cundall, *Hampton Court*, 1930 (detail). Double Royal Poster, 63.5 x 101.6 cm (25 x 40 in.).
7. Arthur Blunt, *Hampton Court*, 1912. Double Crown Poster, 50.8 x 76.2 cm (20 x 30 in.).
8. Elijah Albert Cox, *Hampton Court by Tram*, 1916 (detail). Double Crown Poster, 50.8 x 76.2 cm (20 x 30 in.).
9. Austin Cooper, *Visit the Great Hall and the King's Wine Cellars; Hampton Court*, 1931 (detail). Double Royal Poster, 63.5 x 101.6 cm (25 x 40 in.).
10. Clive Gardiner, *Hampton Court*, 1927 (detail). Double Royal Poster, 63.5 x 101.6 cm (25 x 40 in.).
11. Frederick Charles Herrick, *Hampton Court; Romance and Gaiety*, 1926 (detail). Double Royal Poster, 63.5 x 101.6 cm (25 x 40 in.).
12. Hayward Young, *For Hampton Court*, 1912 (detail). Double Royal Poster, 63.5 x 101.6 cm (25 x 40 in.).
13. Fred Taylor, *Hampton Court*, 1914. Double Crown Poster, 50.8 x 76.2 cm (20 x 30 in.).
14. Alfred Robert Hayward, *Hampton Court*, 1925 (detail). Double Royal Poster, 63.5 x 101.6 cm (25 x 40 in.).
15. Fred Taylor, *Hampton Court*, 1929 (detail). Double Crown Poster, 50.8 x 76.2 cm (20 x 30 in.).
16. Terrick John Williams, *Hampton Court*, 1929 (detail). Double Royal Poster, 63.5 x 101.6 cm (25 x 40 in.).
17. Adrian Allinson, *Hampton Court*, 1934. Double Royal Poster, 63.5 x 101.6 cm (25 x 40 in.).
18. Unknown artist, *The Privy Garden and Palace, Hampton Court*, 1912 (detail). Panel Poster, 21.6 x 52.1 cm (8½ x 20½ in.).
19. Frederic Henri Kay Henrion, *Hampton Court Maze*, 1956 (detail). Double Royal Poster, 63.5 x 101.6 cm (25 x 40 in.).
20. Fred Taylor, *Hampton Court*, 1929 (detail). Double Crown Poster, 50.8 x 76.2 cm (20 x 30 in.).
21. W. Langlands, *Hampton Court*, 1930 (detail). Double Royal Poster, 63.5 x 101.6 cm (25 x 40 in.).
22. George Edward Kruger Gray and Dorothy Hutton, *Historical London No. 2; Hampton Court*, 1922 (detail). Double Royal Poster, 63.5 x 101.6 cm (25 x 40 in.).

Pomegranate Communications, Inc.
Box 808022, Petaluma CA 94975
800 227 1428   www.pomegranate.com

Pomegranate Europe Ltd.
Unit I, Heathcote Business Centre, Hurlbutt Road
Warwick, Warwickshire CV34 6TD, UK
[+44] 0 1926 430111
sales@pomeurope.co.uk

Color illustrations ✪ ® © 2012 Transport for London.
Line drawings © Pomegranate Communications, Inc.

Catalog No. CB143

Designed by Gina Bostian and Oky Sulistio

Printed in Korea

21 20 19 18 17 16 15 14 13 12   10 9 8 7 6 5 4 3 2 I

This product is in compliance with the Consumer Product Safety Improvement Act of 2008 (CPSIA).
A General Conformity Certificate concerning Pomegranate's compliance with the CPSIA is available on our website at www.pomegranate.com, or by request at 800 227 1428.
For additional CPSIA-required tracking details, contact Pomegranate at 800 227 1428.

1. John Hassall, *Hampton Court*

2. Charles Paine, *Hampton Court*

3. Dorothy Paton, *By Tram to Hampton Court*

HAMPTON COURT BY TRAM

4. Arthur Blunt, *Hampton Court by Tram*

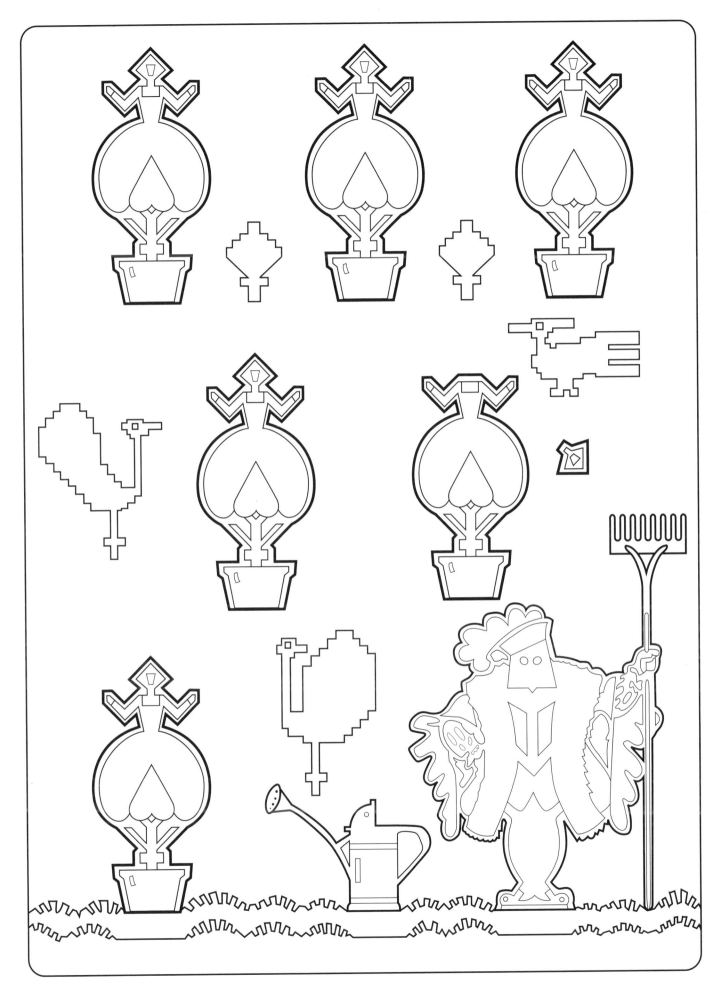

5. Charles Paine, *Hampton Court by Tram*

6. Charles Ernest Cundall, *Hampton Court*

7. Arthur Blunt, *Hampton Court*

8. Elijah Albert Cox, *Hampton Court by Tram*

9. Austin Cooper, *Visit the Great Hall and the King's Wine Cellars; Hampton Court*

10. Clive Gardiner, *Hampton Court*

11. Frederick Charles Herrick, *Hampton Court; Romance and Gaiety*

12. Hayward Young, *For Hampton Court*

13. Fred Taylor, *Hampton Court*

HAMPTON COURT

14. Alfred Robert Hayward, *Hampton Court*

15. Fred Taylor, *Hampton Court*

16. Terrick John Williams, *Hampton Court*

17. Adrian Allinson, *Hampton Court*

18. Unknown artist, *The Privy Garden and Palace, Hampton Court*

19. Frederic Henri Kay Henrion, *Hampton Court Maze*

20. Fred Taylor, *Hampton Court*

21. W. Langlands, *Hampton Court*